RED
IS
NEVER
A
MOUSE

Dear Boys and Girls,

My Weekly Reader is happy to present this delightful book to you. You will laugh at the funny animals. You will enjoy repeating

"Red is never, no never, a mouse."

We hope you will enjoy *Red Is Never a Mouse* as much as we have.

Eleanor M. Johnson
Editor in Chief of My Weekly Reader

RED

THE **BOBBS-MERRILL** COMPANY, INC.
A SUBSIDIARY OF HOWARD W. SAMS & CO., INC.
1720 EAST 38TH STREET · INDIANAPOLIS 6, INDIANA

IS NEVER A MOUSE

by ETH CLIFFORD
Illustrated by BILL HECKLER

Do
you
know
what
RED
is?

RED is a rose,
a brick wall,
or an awning.

RED is the tip
of your tongue
when you're
yawning.

RED is a bump
when a child
takes a fall.

RED is "Watch OUT!
There is danger
for all!"

RED is a fire
truck inside
a fire house . . .

BUT . . . RED IS NEVER,

NO NEVER, A MOUSE!

Do
you
know
what
GREEN
is?

GREEN is an emerald,
a frog,
or a mitten.

GREEN is the look
from the eyes
of a kitten.

GREEN is a leaf,
or a cabbage,
or peas.

GREEN is a pickle
or moss
around trees.

GREEN is the dragon
you wouldn't
ride by on . . .

BUT GREEN IS NEVER,

NO NEVER, A LION!

Do
you
know
what
BLUE
is?

BLUE is a jay
or a bottle
of ink.

BLUE is a berry
you eat
in a wink.

BLUE is the ribbon
for winning
first prize.

BLUE is a bluebell
or clear
summer skies.

BLUE is the water
for sailing
a boat . . .

BUT...BLUE IS NEVER,

NO NEVER, A GOAT!

Do
you
know
what
ORANGE
is?

ORANGE is the autumn
when leaves
blaze the sky.

ORANGE is a pumpkin
that's winking
its eye.

ORANGE is the sun
as it sinks
in the West.

ORANGE is the carrot
all rabbits
like best.

ORANGE is the juice
that will keep
you quite hale . . .

BUT ORANGE IS NEVER,

NO NEVER, A WHALE!

Do
you
know
what
PURPLE
is?

PURPLE'S a clover
or mountains
at night.

PURPLE'S a violet
that's hiding
from sight.

PURPLE'S a grape
or the robe
of a king.

PURPLE'S an eggplant
or lilacs
in spring.

PURPLE'S a plum
that's so juicy
and fat . . .

GRAPE JELLY

BUT **PURPLE** IS NEVER,

NO NEVER, A CAT!

Do
you
know
what
WHITE
is?

WHITE is a lily,
or sugar,
or thread.

WHITE is a cloud,
floating by
overhead.

WHITE is a beard
or a bottle
of milk.

WHITE is a bride,
dressed in satins
and silk.

WHITE is a ghost,
or a swan,
or the snow . . .

BUT WHITE IS NEVER,

NO NEVER, A CROW!

Do
you
know
what
BLACK
is?

BLACK is the night
when the stars
are not out.

BLACK is the crow
who is flying
about.

BLACK is the coal
or an ant
crawling past.

BLACK is a
thunderstorm
coming up
fast.

BLACK is a shoe
or a witch's
mean laugh . . .

BUT **BLACK** IS NEVER,

NO NEVER, A GIRAFFE!

Now,
starting at A,
all the way down to Z,
List all of the colors
in things that you see.

At first you will think
it is easy for you,
But it will take weeks,
or much longer, to do.

And then when you've finished,
you'll have to agree . . .

A

RED

mouse

you never,

no never,

did see!